Kim
and the
missing
paint pot

Written by Miriam Moss

Illustrated by Peet Ellison

Heinemann

One day Kim was in the classroom
working on the computer. She was
making a picture of a house. On the
screen were lots of paint pots.
'I think I'll paint the roof red,'
said Kim.
But when she looked for the red paint
pot, it had gone.

Suddenly the computer screen went red, then blue, then green, and a little face appeared.

'Hello Kim,' it said. 'I am Bleep. I can help you to find the red paint pot. Shut your eyes and come with me.'

So Kim shut her eyes ...

'Where am I?' asked Kim when she
opened her eyes again.
'You are inside the computer,'
said Bleep.
Kim could see a house.
'That's the house from my picture!'
she said.

Just then a giant paintbrush ran by.
He was painting everything green.
'Why is he doing that?' asked Kim.
'Because he's cross about his missing
    paint pot,' said Bleep. 'We must find
    it before he paints us green too.'
Bleep looked at the computer menu
and pushed the key that said Pictures.

A door appeared and Kim and Bleep
went through.

'This is where all the people from your
picture books live,' said Bleep.

'Come on, let's find out if anyone has
seen the missing paint pot.'

First they met the
Three Billy Goats.
They had spots of
green paint all
over them.

Then they met the
Gingerbread Man.
He had spots of
green paint all
over him too.

Then they met
Cinderella and she
had spots of green
paint all over her
dress.

But no one had seen the missing
red paint pot.

'Come on,' said Bleep. 'We must go on looking.'

So off they went into a forest.

Soon they came to a cottage. Just
outside the cottage they saw a little girl
and her grandmother.

'Look,' said Kim. 'It's Little Red
Riding Hood.'

The little girl was opening a present.
It was a beautiful doll's house ... and
it was painted RED.

Little Red Riding Hood asked Kim
and Bleep into the house for tea ...

... and there, on the table, was a
big red paint pot.

'That's the missing paint pot!' said
Kim. 'We've been looking everywhere
for it.'

'Oh dear,' said Grandmother. 'I took
it so that I could paint the doll's house.
Little Red Riding Hood likes
everything to be red.'

'We'll take the paint pot back for you,'
said Kim and Bleep.

So Grandmother put the paint pot in a
basket and waved them off.

'Look out for the wolf,' she called.

Kim and Bleep ran back through the
forest and gave the red paint pot back
to Paintbrush.

'Now you must stop painting spots on
everything,' said Bleep.

'And I must go and paint my house,'
said Kim.

Just then everything went red, then blue, then green. Suddenly Kim was back in the classroom, just as the bell went for going-home time.

Kim's teacher, Mrs Morris, came over to the computer.

'That's a good picture,' she said. 'But you must turn the computer off now. It's time to go home.'

Kim took one last look at her picture.

Someone was painting the roof.

It was Bleep.